# BÉLA BARTÓK
## CONCERTO
### FOR ORCHESTRA

D0956215

## BOOSEY & HAWKES
### LTD.

LONDON · PARIS · BONN · JOHANNESBURG · SYDNEY · TORONTO · BUENOS AIRES · NEW YORK

NET PRICE

MADE IN ENGLAND

*First performance on December 1st, 1944, by
the Boston Symphony Orchestra under the direction of
Dr. Serge Koussevitzky, at Carnegie Hall, New York.*

## INSTRUMENTATION

3 Flutes (3rd doubling Piccolo)
3 Oboes (3rd doubling Cor Anglais)
3 Clarinets in B*b* and A (3rd doubling Bass Clarinet)
3 Bassoons (3rd doubling Double Bassoon)
4 Horns in F
3 Trumpets in C (4th Trumpet ad lib.)
2 Tenor Trombones
Bass Trombone
Tuba
Timpani
Side Drum
Bass Drum
Tam-Tam
Cymbals
Triangle
2 Harps
Strings

*Duration :* approximately 37 minutes

Written for the Koussevitzky Music Foundation in memory of Mrs. Natalie Koussevitzky

# CONCERTO FOR ORCHESTRA

## I
### (INTRODUZIONE)

BÉLA BARTÓK

Copyright 1946 in U.S.A. by Hawkes & Son (London), Ltd.
Copyright for all countries

All rights reserved
Tous droits reservés
B. & H. 9009

*) always use a soft (cardboard) mute.

near the sound-board with an appropriately
shaped wooden (if possible metal) stick

438

438

Duration of 1st movement approx. 9'45"

# II
## (GIUOCO DELLE COPPIE)

36

44

Duration of 2nd movement approx. 6'17"

# III
## (ELEGIA)

48

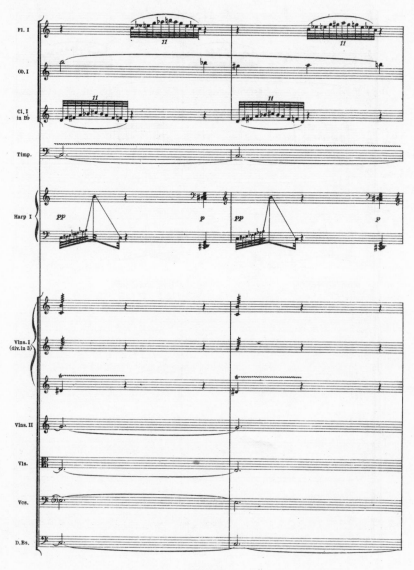

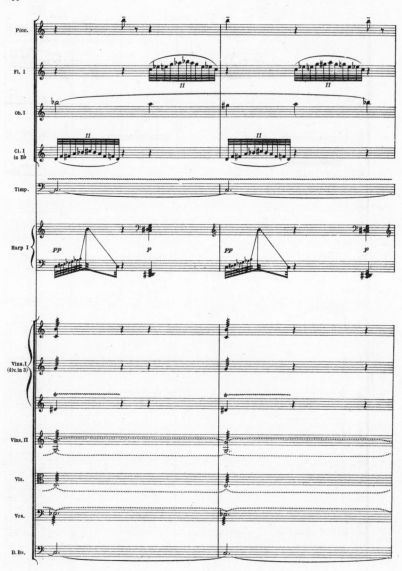

62

64

B.& H. 9009

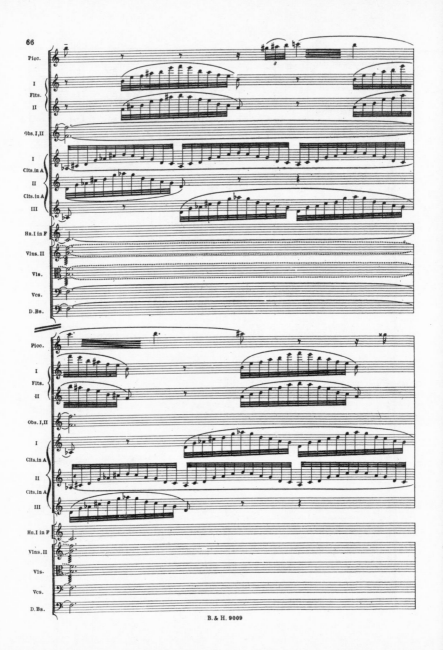

Duration of 3rd movement approx. 7' 11"

# IV
## (INTERMEZZO INTERROTTO)

* If the Flute has no low ♭, 1st Bassoon will play: and Flute tacet.

* real sound:

B. & H. 9009

Duration of 4th movement approx. 4' 8"

# V
## (FINALE)

*always non spiccato (i.e. legato)

B. & H. 9009

B.& H. 9009

86

B & H. 9009

110

B. & H. 9009

339
344
pochiss. rall. a tempo
I
Flts.
II
I
Obs.
II
I
Clts. in B♭
II
Bsn. I
Harp I
339
344
pochiss. rall. a tempo
Vlns. I
(div.)
Vlns. II
(div.)
unis.
Vls.
mp
unis.
Vcs.

126

* as near the bridge as possible.

B. & H. 9009

138

B. & H. 9009

144

Duration of 5th movement approx. 8′52″
Duration of the whole work ca. 37′

1943, aug. 15 – okt. 8

*Alternative ending*

B.& H. 9009

Lowe and Brydone (Printers) Limited, London

# Hawkes Pocket Scores

### A selection of outstanding modern works
### from this famous library of classical and contemporary Pocket Scores

| No. | **Béla Bartók** |
|---|---|
| 28 | Divertimento *for String Orchestra* |
| 79 | Concerto for Orchestra |
| 100 | Concerto No. 3 *for Piano and Orchestra* |
| 607 | Suite No. 2, Op. 4 *(Revised 1943 Edition)* |
| 657 | Rhapsody No. 1 *for Violin and Orchestra* |
| 658 | Rhapsody No. 2 *for Violin and Orchestra* |

**Arthur Bliss**
690 A Colour Symphony

**Alexander Borodin**
45 Danses Polovtsiennes *from 'Prince Igor'*
673 Prince Igor *Overture*

**Benjamin Britten**
38 Sinfonia da Requiem, Op. 20
39 Les Illuminations, Op. 18
63 Saint Nicolas *Cantata*, Op. 42
64 Variations on a Theme of Frank Bridge
71 Serenade, Op. 31
83 Four Sea Interludes, Op. 33a
        *from 'Peter Grimes'*
84 Passacaglia, Op. 33b *from 'Peter Grimes'*
606 The Young Person's Guide to the
        Orchestra, Op. 34

**Aaron Copland**
49 El Salón México
72 Billy the Kid
82 Appalachian Spring
676 An Outdoor Overture
684 Four Dance Episodes *from 'Rodeo'*
685 Statements

**Frederick Delius**
41 Appalachia
43 Sea Drift

**Gerald Finzi**
97 Dies Natalis *Cantata*

**Gustav Holst**
22 The Planets

**John Ireland**
16 A London Overture

**Dmitri Kabalevsky**
74 Colas Breugnon *Overture*

**Zoltán Kodály**
683 Kálló Folk Dances

**Modeste Moussorgsky**
653 A Night on the Bare Mountain

**Moussorgsky–Ravel**
No.
32 Tableaux d'une Exposition

**Serge Prokofieff**
24 March and Scherzo *from*
        'The Love of the Three Oranges'
33 Symphonie Classique, Op. 25
52 Piano Concerto No. 3, C Major, Op. 26
95 Symphony No. 5, Op. 100
660 Cinderella Suite No. 1, Op. 107
663 Lieutenant Kijé, Suite, Op. 60

**Nicolas Rimsky-Korsakoff**
34 Schéhérazade, Op. 35
36 Capriccio Espagnol, Op. 34

**Richard Strauss**
99 Metamorphosen
645 Oboe Concerto
646 Duet-Concertino
        *for Clarinet, Bassoon, Strings and Harp*
662 Horn Concerto No. 2
667 Vier letzte Lieder (Four Last Songs)
677 Symphonie für Bläser

**Igor Strawinsky**
610 Capriccio *(Revised 1949 Edition)*
611 Apollon Musagète *(Revised 1947 Edition)*
630 Octet *for Wind Instruments*
        *(Revised 1952 Edition)*
632 Pulcinella Suite *(Revised 1949 Edition)*
637 Symphony of Psalms
638 The Rite of Spring *(Revised 1947 Edition)*
639 Pétrouchka *(Revised 1947 Edition)*
640 Orpheus
651 Œdipus Rex *(Revised 1948 Edition)*
652 Perséphone
655 Mass
666 Cantata
672 Symphonies of Wind Instruments
        *(Revised 1947 Edition)*
679 The Fairy's Kiss
682 Septet (1953)
688 In Memoriam Dylan Thomas (1954)

**Ralph Vaughan Williams**
59 Fantasia on a Theme by Thomas Tallis
60 The Wasps *Overture*

*The complete catalogue available from the publishers on request*

# Boosey & Hawkes
### Limited
295 Regent Street, London, W.1
Paris · Bonn · Johannesburg · Sydney · Toronto · Buenos Aires · New York

No. 782

1.56